THE ODD SQUAD

BY ALLAN PLENDERLEITH

RAVETTE PUBLISHING

First published in 2002
Reprinted in 2003, 2004, 2005, 2006
Ravette Publishing Limited
Unit 3, Tristar Centre
Star Road, Partridge Green
West Sussex RH13 8RA

Printed in Malta by Gutenberg Press

ISBN: 978-1-84161-139-6

PINE
FRESH
PINE
FRESH

MAUDE WAS SAD
TO DISCOVER
HER BUM HAD
MOVED SOUTH.

GREETINGS FROM THE
SOUTH
POLE!

BY APPLYING
LIPSTICK TO HER
DOUBLE CHIN, LILY
SCARES THE LOCAL
KIDS WITH HER
'EXTRA MOUTH'
ROUTINE.

AAAAEEEE!!

LILY PROMISED NEXT TIME SHE RODE THE BIKE TO WEAR HER 'BOOB CLIPS'.

IN THEIR LATER YEARS, SOME WOMEN RESORT TO DESPERATE MEASURES TO BANISH WRINKLES.

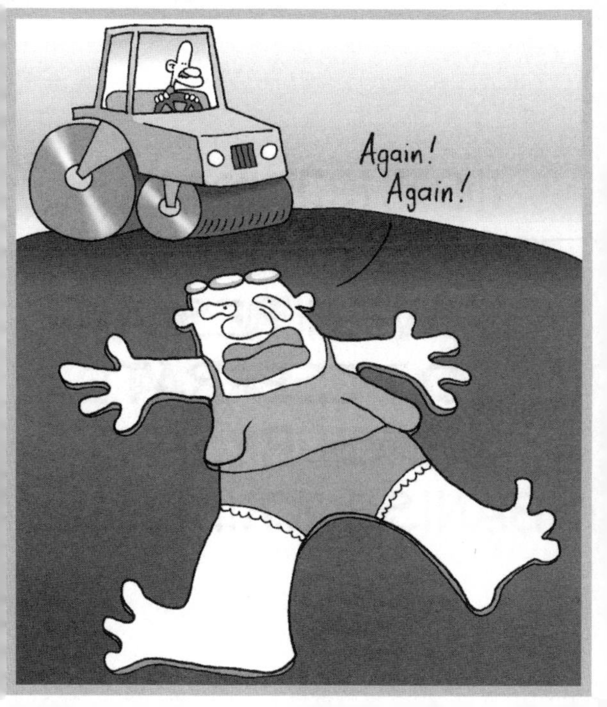
Again!
Again!

ON HOLIDAY, LILY HAD A SURE-FIRE WAY TO CLEAR A SPACE BY THE POOL.

B-BOOM!

UNABLE TO
AFFORD THE
HEATING BILLS
DURING THE
WINTER, LILY
AND ALF
SIMPLY SPRAY
THEMSELVES
WITH DEEP HEAT.

PSHH!
OW!
AP.

AS WOMEN
GROW OLDER,
THEIR CHOICE
OF PERFUME
CHANGES.

Awwwh!
My favourite!
EAU
de
PEE

LILY ACCIDENTALLY WALKS OVER AN AIR VENT.

LILY HAS AN EMBARRASSING EXPERIENCE ON THE BUS.

Excuse me, you're sitting on my left boob.
H

WHENEVER SHE HAS LOTS OF MAIL TO SEND, MAUDE VISITS HER AUNT MATILDA.

DROOL!

ALTHOUGH HE WAS
OLD, ALF COULD
STILL GET IT UP.

CLICK
WHIRR
10 kg
WOOP!
CLAP!
CLAP!
CLAP!

ALF HADN'T
THE HEART TO
TELL LILY THE
'HAMSTER' SHE
FOUND IN THE
BATH WAS
ACTUALLY
THE SOAP.

LILY DIDN'T MIND THE KIDS PLAYING WITH HER KNICKERS, IF ONLY THEY WEREN'T USING THEM AS AN AIRCRAFT HANGAR.

AS HE GREW OLDER, ALF BEGAN TO HAVE TROUBLE WITH HIS JOINTS.

AP.

MAUDE COULD
STILL GET INTO
THAT LEOPARD
SKIN MINI SKIRT
SHE USED TO
WEAR AS A
TEENAGER.

AS JEFF WALKED INTO THE ROOM UNEXPECTEDLY, HE HAD A FEELING LILY AND ALF HAD BEEN UP TO SOMETHING.

IT HAPPENED ON
A TUESDAY
AFTERNOON
AROUND 4:15,
LILY'S BODY
FINALLY GIVES UP
ITS BATTLE WITH
GRAVITY.

SPLOSH!

COOL! IT WAS
SO COLD ALF
COULD SEE
LILY'S NIPPLES.

OLD LADIES'
BOOBS: NATURE'S
BUILT-IN
SCARVES!

THE REAL REASON WHY OLD PEOPLE CAN ALWAYS BE FOUND QUEUING.

POST OFFICE
TEE HEE
OOOH!
GROPE!
FONDLE!
FEEL!
SQUEEZE!

AS THEY GROW
OLDER, MEN
MOVE FROM
COMPARING
PENIS SIZE TO
EAR SIZE.

Mine are bigger!
No, MINE are!!

IRONICALLY THE OLDER AND WEAKER YOU GET, THE STRONGER YOUR FARTS BECOME.

LILY CATCHES
ALF LOOKING
AT ANOTHER
WOMAN'S BOOBS.

LILY AND ALF
DISCOVER THE
PERILS OF
WEARING TOO
MUCH POLYESTER.

I CAN'T GET DOWN!
BBZZZ!
CRACKLE!
BZZT!

PILES ARE NOT
SO BAD IF YOU
SEE THEM AS
BUILT-IN
BEAN BAGS.

WITH HIS LATEST GIFT, LILY GOT THE FEELING ALF WAS TRYING TO TELL HER SOMETHING.

PINE
FRESH
PINE
FRESH

NEVER
BLOW-OFF
IN SUPPORT
TIGHTS.

FARP
POW!
BUS STOP

ALF KNEW TO
LEAVE LILY
ALONE WHEN SHE
WAS GOING
THROUGH
'THE CHANGE'.

DURING THEIR
LOVE-MAKING,
LILY AND ALF
BECOME
ENTANGLED.

WHENEVER TOM
JONES COMES ON
THE RADIO, LILY
GETS CARRIED
AWAY.

NOT EVEN THE PARROT COULD TAKE ANY MORE OF LILY AND ALF REPEATING THEMSELVES.

And I remember the time when I did something...
Oh yes, it was on a Tuesday or was it....

TO GIVE
HERSELF A MORE
YOUTHFUL
APPEARANCE, LILY
TIES HER HAIR
BACK IN A
TIGHT BUN.

WAAAAAA!
AP.

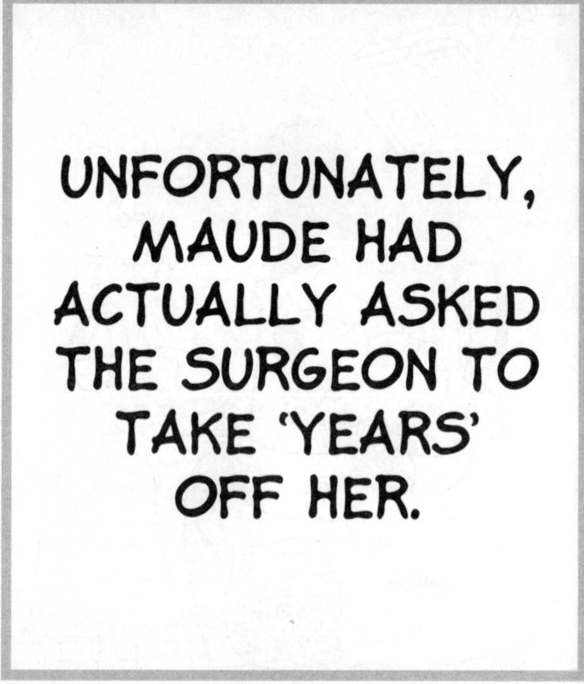

UNFORTUNATELY, MAUDE HAD ACTUALLY ASKED THE SURGEON TO TAKE 'YEARS' OFF HER.

SADLY, IT WOULD
BE SOME HOURS
LATER BEFORE
THE TAXI DRIVER
NOTICED LILY HAD
TRAPPED HER
BOOB IN THE
CAR DOOR.

TAXI

HOPING FOR
SOME FUN, ALF
ASKED THE NURSE
FOR A SPONGE
BATH.

ALTHOUGH TO A
BYSTANDER IT
LOOKED LIKE ALF
WAS TYING LILY'S
SHOELACES, HE
WAS IN FACT
FEELING HER
BOOBS.

TEE
HEE
HEE

ONCE AGAIN,
LILY HAD
SOMETHING
STUCK IN HER
TEETH.

WHEN YOU GET OLDER, SHORTS AND SHORT DRESSES ARE NO LONGER AN OPTION.

JANICE WAS WRONG – MAUDE <u>COULD</u> STILL GET INTO A SIZE 12.

FAR FROM SAGGY BOOBS BEING A BURDEN, THEY CAN BECOME HANDY HOLDERS FOR CIGARETTES AND PENCILS.

HAVING FAILED TO TALK THE BANK MANAGER INTO GIVING HER A LOAN, LILY TRIES OUT THE OLD 'SHARON STONE LEG CROSSING TECHNIQUE'.

AS A SPECIAL TREAT, ALF GIVES LILY A RELAXING FOOT MASSAGE.

HAVING RUN OUT
OF MARZIPAN,
LILY OPTS FOR
AN ALTERNATIVE.

SQUELCH
SLURP
GARGLE
FLOUR

A GREAT
ANIMAL LOVER,
LILY ALWAYS
TOPS UP
THE BIRD FOOD
IN THE WINTER.

BOKE!
GAG!
CHIK!
SNIP!
CRACK!

WHEN YOU'RE OLD
IT'S TEMPTING
JUST TO STAY IN
AND WATCH THE
CRAP ON TV.

SUDDENLY, SANTA REALISES HE HAS STUMBLED INTO A 'GRANNY TRAP'.

CLUNK!
CLUNK!

ODD SQUAD titles available...

Title		ISBN	Price
I Love Beer!	(hardcover)	978-1-84161-238-6	£4.99
I Love Dad!	(hardcover)	978-1-84161-252-2	£4.99
I Love Mum!	(hardcover)	978-1-84161-249-2	£4.99
I Love Poo!	(hardcover)	978-1-84161-240-9	£4.99
I Love Sex!	(hardcover)	978-1-84161-241-6	£4.99
I Love Wine!	(hardcover)	978-1-84161-239-3	£4.99
I Love Xmas!	(hardcover)	978-1-84161-262-1	£4.99
The Little Book of Booze		978-1-84161-138-9	£2.50
The Little Book of Men		978-1-84161-093-1	£2.50
The Little Book of Oldies		978-1-84161-139-6	£2.50
The Little Book of Poo		978-1-84161-096-2	£2.50
The Little Book of Pumping		978-1-84161-140-2	£2.50
The Little Book of Sex		978-1-84161-095-5	£2.50
The Little Book of Women		978-1-84161-094-8	£2.50
The Little Book of X-Rated Cartoons		978-1-84161-141-9	£2.50
Big Poo Handbook	(hardcover)	978-1-84161-168-6	£7.99
Sexy Sex Manual	(hardcover)	978-1-84161-220-1	£7.99
The Odd Squad Butt Naked		978-1-84161-190-7	£3.99
The Odd Squad Gross Out!		978-1-84161-219-5	£3.99
The Odd Squad's Saggy Bits		978-1-84161-218-8	£3.99
The REAL Kama Sutra		978-1-84161-103-7	£3.99
The Odd Squad Volume One		978-1-85304-936-1	£3.99

HOW TO ORDER ... Please send a cheque/postal order in £ sterling, made payable to 'Ravette Publishing' for the cover price of the books and allow the following for postage and packing...

UK & BFPO	70p for the first book & 40p per book thereafter
Europe & Eire	£1.30 for the first book & 70p per book thereafter
Rest of the world	£2.20 for the first book & £1.10 per book thereafte

RAVETTE PUBLISHING Unit 3, Tristar Centre, Star Road, Partridge Green, West Sussex RH13 8RA

Prices and availability are subject to change without prior notice.